About the story

Penny love finding out about things. This stor
learnt about borrowing. Penny and her friend:
other all the time, such as pencils, CDs and e
out that adults borrow too. They borrow mone

In the story, your child will be introduced to the concept of borrowing money to afford things they want or need, but don't have enough money to buy straight away. Your child will discover you can borrow money in various ways and will be introduced to credit cards, loans and paying interest on money that is borrowed. They will also learn the importance of only borrowing what they can afford to pay back.

Reading the story

Read the story with your child. Stop whenever you feel it's right, to ask questions, to ask what might happen next, to tell of your experiences or to answer questions from your child. Or you may read the whole story together first and then talk about it. Do treat it as fun!

You may also wish to share your own experiences of borrowing money; however, you may not want to share too much information with your child, but enough to prompt discussion and to show that you have had the same experiences of money as Penny.

THE STORY

Penny Wise Finds Out About Borrowing

This is my family...

This is me. My name is Penelope Wise, but my friends just call me Penny.

This is my Dad. He is always borrowing my CDs to use in the car.

This is my Mum. She is always borrowing my i-pod so that she can dance around the house while she is clearning.

And this is my smelly little brother Fred. I don't let him borrow anything because he breaks everything!

I love finding out about things. This book is all about the time I learned about ...

... borrowing.

My friends and I borrow each other's things all the time ...

pencils ...

 CDs ...

DVDs ...

 ... and even clothes

But I found out that grown-ups borrow something else ...

... money!

One Friday in school I was in the playground when I saw my teacher, Mr Bosco, looking very sad. I wanted to ask him what was wrong but he was talking to the Headteacher.

This is my teacher, Mr Bosco. He is usually a very happy chap.

I didn't hear everything he said but what I did hear did not sound good.

... Car broke down again... Garage can't fix it... too old... alone...

This sounded terrible. His car can't be fixed and he's feeling old and lonely! Perhaps he cannot visit his friends because his car is broken! I told my friends. They thought that we should do something to cheer him up.

Poor Mr Bosco! We could make him a special 'cheer up teacher' card

Or we could make him something. I know! A model car.

O.K. Let's do it after school today. Then we can give them to him on Monday!

This is Maria. She always thinks of good ideas.

This is Leo. He always tries to help but he is not that great at good ideas.

After school we went round to Maria's house to make things to cheer him up.

Maria made the card using lots of glitter, fabric and paint.
(She is very careful.)

Leo made a model of Mr Bosco's old car, using lots of card, paint and glue. (He is not that brilliant at being careful.)

And I wrote a poem to cheer Mr Bosco up. We stuck it inside the card.

If your car is broken down
And you can't see your mates.
You don't have to wear a frown
'Cos I'll lend you my in-line skates.

We were all very pleased with our work. Maria said that she would look after the card and the car and would bring them to school tomorrow.

When I got home we had a DISASTER! The television broke down! We were watching our favourite programme, 'I want to be a singer'. In it lots of people sing songs and you vote for your favourite singer.

They were just about to reveal who had been voted the best singer when ...

... the screen went blank!

We tried everything to fix it but it did not help.

Mum tried pressing
the 'on' button on
the remote control
REALLY hard!

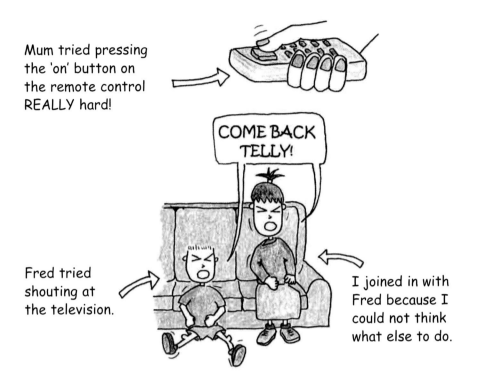

Fred tried
shouting at
the television.

I joined in with
Fred because I
could not think
what else to do.

Dad offered to fix it but Mum said NO!
(Dad tried to fix the toaster last week
and it exploded!)

This was terrible! No telly! We could not survive without all our favourite programmes.

Don't worry! We'll go out tomorrow and get a new one.

But a new television will cost a lot of money! It will take AGES to save up enough money!

We don't have to save up for it. I can use my credit card.

A credit card. What's that?

Mum and Dad explained what a credit card was by telling me about our last holiday. It was summer, school was finished, and Mum was finding it difficult to keep us entertained.

MUM! WE'RE BORED!

Mum was getting 'frazzled'!

So Dad decided to book a surprise holiday to cheer us up (and give Mum and Dad a break).

Because Dad didn't have time to save up for the holiday, he paid for it using his credit card. He went on the internet and found a travel agent's website. Mum and Dad booked a week's holiday for the family in a place with lots of fun activities for Fred and me.

Then he typed in his credit card number. It is very long and he had to concentrate very hard.

This is difficult when Fred is around!

The computer told Dad's credit card company that he wanted to borrow money to pay for the holiday. They said that it was o.k. and paid for our holiday.

Everyone had a smashing time on holiday.

Dad spent all day 'working on his tan'.

Mum decided to keep fit.

I learned how to windsurf! Cool!

And Fred spent all week covered up to avoid getting sunburnt.

So whenever we want something we can't afford we can use the credit card?

Oh no! When we borrow the money from the credit card company we have to be able to pay it back. So we only use it when we really have to.

Dad said that every month the credit card company send him a bill. It tells him how much money he has borrowed and how much of the money he has to pay back.

BLUECREDIT
Account Name: Mr A Wise
Account Number: 7777 6966 0707 0865

Credit limit: £3000

This tells Dad how much he is allowed to borrow.

Statement for June

This tells Dad how much he has borrowed.

3 June	Gateway Holidays	£850.00
Interest Added		£ 0.00
Total Amount Borrowed		£850.00
Minimum Payment		£150.00

This tells Dad how much he needs to pay back this month.

Mum explained that this is how Credit Card companies earn their money. They help people to buy things that they want but cannot afford to pay for straight away (like a new television). So if people cannot pay all the money back at the end of the month they charge interest on the money they have not paid back.

So Dad had to pay more because he could not afford to pay it all back at once?

Yes. But if he had not borrowed the money he would not have been able to take us on the holiday.

Why didn't he save up the money for the holiday?

Well he could have but he wanted to take us during the summer. By the time he had saved up the money it would have been winter and the weather wouldn't have been very nice!

So credit cards can be used to get things you want when you want them. Although it means you might pay more for things, you don't miss out on not having them.

If we saved up for a new television it could take a long time. We might have to go without television for months until we could afford it. And that would not be good! Imagine! No telly for months!

So on Saturday we went shopping for a new television. We were all very excited!

FLURRYS
ELECTRICAL SUPERSTORE
IF IT'S GOT A PLUG WE SELL IT!

We looked at all the televisions. There were so many to choose from! Then Dad saw a television which was just what we wanted.

Special Offer
WAS £750
NOW £650

This is me looking amazed.

Mum and Dad found a sales person and he told them all about the television. But as they were talking I saw the most amazing television I had ever seen!

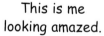

It was HUGE. The screen was as big as my bed! There were four huge speakers and it was like being in a cinema.

I ran back to Mum and Dad to tell them I had found the perfect television.

I managed to drag Mum and Dad and the sales assistant over to the monster television. Everyone was VERY impressed and I dreamt about having all my friends over to watch our favourite DVDs in my very own cinema.

But then Mum and Dad said:

I don't think we can afford this Penny.

No Penny. It is too expensive!

But we can use your credit card! We can borrow the money and pay it back a little at a time! Just like Dad did before!

I was confused! Credit cards let you borrow money to get the things you want. And you don't have to pay it all back straight away. But Mum and Dad would not use the credit card to buy the most amazing television I had ever seen. I was not happy!

This is me looking 'not happy'.

While Dad, Fred and the sales assistant went to the till to buy the cheaper television, Mum took me outside to explain why they had not bought the amazing television.

It would be very easy to buy the home cinema system. But if you borrow too much money it can be very difficult to pay it back.

But we don't have to pay it back all at once. We could pay back a little each month.

Yes but if we buy expensive things using our credit card we could end up borrowing SO MUCH money that we cannot afford to pay it back each month!

Mum said that some people borrow so much money using credit cards that they cannot afford to pay it back!

They end up in something called BAD DEBT!

This is SCARY stuff! If you cannot pay back any of the money that you borrowed, the credit card company can take back the things that you borrowed the money for!

The television!

The car!

Furniture!

Even your house!

And even if you manage to pay it all back, you may NEVER be allowed to borrow money again! So that is why Mum and Dad did not buy the amazing television. It made a lot of sense!

The next day we gave Mr Bosco the card
and the model car. He smiled a big smile.

Mr Bosco started to laugh.
Then he explained why.

Mr Bosco explained that a credit card is not the only way that people can borrow money. They can go to a bank to get a loan. A loan is when you borrow a set amount of money from a bank to buy something that you cannot afford to buy.

So when Mr Bosco's car broke down he went to the bank and asked for a loan to buy a new car.

The bank decided that Mr Bosco could afford to pay the money back and gave him a loan to buy his new car.

The bank will charge him interest on the money that he borrowed (just like the credit card) and work out how much he will have to pay back to the bank each month. Because Mr Bosco can afford the monthly payments to the bank he can buy his car and get to work on time!

When I got home I told my Dad about
Mr Bosco and how he had borrowed money
from the bank to buy his new car.

Sometimes it is the only way
to afford expensive things
that we really need.
We borrowed the money to
buy this house.

Really! But houses
are very expensive.
How did you pay it all
back?

Well we have not paid it all
back yet. We took out a
special type of loan from the
bank. It is called a mortgage.

A mortgage?

Dad explained that when someone wants to buy
somewhere to live, they borrow most of the
money by taking out a mortgage. When they
borrowed the money from the bank they agreed
to pay back part of the money (plus interest) to
the bank each month over 25 years!

After dinner we sat in front of the television to watch another episode of 'I want to be a singer'.

She's a good singer. But that dress looks TERRIBLE!

She's better than the last act. Even Fred can sing better than him!

LA! LA! LA! LA!

What a racket!

But I was thinking about all the borrowing grown-ups do. I found out on the internet that in one month grown-ups borrowed a total of ...

£7,300,000,000!

If people could not borrow money they would not be able to afford things that they really need, like houses and cars. But borrowing can be scary. You should only borrow what you can afford to pay back. Otherwise you could end up in BAD DEBT! And that's NOT GOOD!

Borrowing money

There are lots of different ways to borrow money. They all involve paying back rather more than you borrowed; in some cases, a lot more. You could opt to take out a bank overdraft; use a credit card; take out a bank loan; borrow from a credit union; take out a mortgage; borrow from friends or family, or even use a 'loan shark' – a person or company that lends money at very high interest rates, often when banks and others won't lend it (see page 30).

Credit cards

If you have a credit card you can usually use an overdraft, meaning you can take out more money than is in your account. You are billed once a month and have one month to repay what you've borrowed, or you will have to pay interest. It can helpful to use a credit card in this way, if you have short-term money issues, such as bills to pay before pay day – as long as you pay the amount fully before the month is up.

However, rates of interest are usually a lot higher than if you get a personal loan from a bank. If you need to borrow a large amount of money, the credit card is not the best option and because interest is so high you may end up owing more than you can easily repay.

The rate of interest is indicated by the APR (Annual Percentage Rate), and even if you pay back some of what you owe, the bank will still charge you interest on the whole sum you borrowed in the first place. Therefore, choosing the right credit card with a low APR is vital if you think you may be using your credit card to borrow.

Collect leaflets of different credit cards and compare the interest rates they charge. Work out the interest on a £500 purchase on a credit card. To work out the interest: divide £500 by 100 and multiply the answer by the interest rate. So, if the interest rate was 8%: £500 divided by 100 is £5, multiplied by 8 = £40.

Taking out a loan

If you've decided that you might want to borrow money, you need first to think about whether you can afford to. It may seem like a silly question – who can't afford to borrow? But it can be one of the quickest ways of spiralling into debt if you find yourself unable to pay the money back.

Once you've worked out your budget and decided that borrowing could help you sort out your finances, you'll want to decide how you want to borrow.

There are several different types of loan:

Secured loan
If, for example, you were to take out a loan in order to buy a car, the bank might offer you a secured loan. This means that if you were unable to keep up with your repayments, the bank could force you to sell the car. Another example of a secured loan is your mortgage. Similarly, the ownership of your house is at risk if you don't pay it on time. Seeing as these loans are less risky for the lender, they are usually cheaper and have a lower rate of interest.

Unsecured loan
In this case, a bank lends you money and relies on you promising to pay them back. Because this is more risky for them, interest rates are higher. Usually you agree to repay the loan over a set period of time. If you decide to pay it quicker than agreed, penalties sometimes apply! Unsecured loans are suitable for the short-term, especially 1-5 years.

Credit Union loan
If you belong to a Credit Union and have proven yourself to be a reliable saver, they may lend you what they know you will be able to repay. Membership of a Credit Union means that this is a more personal kind of loan as you are part of a kind of club, but they are regulated by the Financial Services Authority (FSA), who are also there to protect your money just as if it were kept in a bank or building society.

Debt

You do need to be very careful when making the decision to borrow money. No matter how good your financial situation, your situation can change. You may have borrowed money based on the fact that you know you can pay it back, but then things change.

Some may decide it's never worth buying using credit because it isn't worth the risk; others feel borrowing should be a last resort. However, if you've made the decision to go ahead, or have borrowed and found yourself unable to make the repayments, here are a few things you might find helpful to know.

Good Debt vs Bad Debt

Sometimes people refer to 'good debts' and 'bad debts'. Not all debt is bad; sometimes it's necessary to get into debt. A mortgage is an example of good debt, because even though you are making repayments for a long time on the property it is paying for, its value could grow a great deal within that time.

Bad debt is when you owe money that you may not be able to repay. This amount will grow bigger the longer you leave it because it will be earning interest all the time, possibly at quite a high rate.

If you don't know what to do about your debt there are lots of places you can go for advice. The website www.moneysavingexpert.com is packed with information, including how you might be able to reduce the amount you are paying. Part of this advice will be budgeting your way out of your problem.

If you have several credit cards (and store cards), you could lose track of what you owe so it might be a good idea to transfer all your credit card debts onto one card, at the best possible APR. Of course, you can't do that with store cards though you might borrow money to pay off the store card debts at a cheaper interest rate.

The UK is very lucky; there are many places you can go to get free, independent advice on how to get out of debt. Here are just a few;
- Citizens Advice Bureau – www.adviceguide.org.uk
- National Debtline www.nationaldebtline.co.uk – 0808 808 4000
- Consumer Credit Counselling Service – www.cccs.co.uk
- Debt Advice Foundation –
  www.debtadvicefoundation.org/talk-about-debt – 0800 644 60 89

Never, ever use a loan shark. As the name suggests, loan sharks are not there to help you out. They may appear to be helpful in that they are willing to lend money, but the rate of interest they charge is huge and you will probably end up in a lot more debt than you were before.

The government estimates that up to 200,000 people in the UK owe money to loan sharks. What they do is treated as a serious criminal offence because of links to organised crime and violence.

If you don't manage your finances and understand what you can and cannot afford, it is easier than ever to spiral into debt. If you are already heavily in debt, the important thing is to find a way out of the red and into the black, and to tackle the problem as soon as you possibly can. Whatever you do, don't shoulder the burden by yourself. Telling somebody else will help you put things in perspective and encourage you to get on with dealing with your debts.

Steps to take

- Gather statements that detail how much you owe and who you owe it to.
- From these, work out exactly how much you owe. Don't panic, it's just a number; any amount can be dealt with once you are organised.
- Decide which debts should take priority. Below shows how the government thinks debt should be dealt with:

Priority Debts	Debts
Mortgage repayments	Credit card and store card payments
Secured loans	Bank loans
Rent	Overdrafts
Council Tax	Catalogue repayments
Utility Bills	Money borrowed from family/friends
Taxes	
Court fines	